DR XARGLE'S
BOOK OF
EARTHLET SLEEPOVERS

Translated into Human by Jeanne Willis
Pictures by Tony Ross

In association with DryNites® Pyjama Pants

This edition has been specially produced by Andersen Press
for Kimberly-Clark for promotional purposes only. Not for resale.
DryNites® is a Registered Trademark of Kimberly-Clark Worldwide, Inc.

The characters in this book are based on the *Dr Xargle* series:
Dr Xargle's Book of Earthlets, Dr Xargle's Book of Earth Hounds,
Dr Xargle's Book of Earth Tiggers, Dr Xargle's Book of Earth Relations,
Dr Xargle's Book of Earth Weather and *Dr Xargle's Book of Earth Mobiles*
published by Andersen Press, London SW1V 2SA
ISBN 1 84270 450 8

Good morning, Class. Today we are going to learn about Earthlet Sleepovers. A sleepover is when an Earthlet invites all its friends to stay awake for as long as possible.

To arrange a sleepover, first the Earthlet must force
the Parent Earthlings to say yes.
If they say no, the Earthlet must:
a) Threaten to leave the earth dwelling forever and ever.
b) Stamp its tentacles and squirt salty water from its
two squinty eyes.

If the Parent Earthlings say yes, the Earthlet must make a list of the noisiest, rudest, silliest Earthlets in the universe and invite them all. For a good sleepover, invite enough Earthlets to snap the legs on your bed.

Here are the rules for some Earthlet Sleepover games:
1. Stinkparp: The idea is to make the loudest, smelliest explosions under the bed covering. The first one to open the window is the loser.

2. Sneezefluff: Players must attack each other with bags of birdfluff until the stuffing fills the atmosphere. The winner is the one whose nose explodes loudest.

3. Musical Earthlings: The players must play their music loudly until the Parent Earthlings burst into the room, shaking their tentacles angrily. The winner is the first to make the Next-Door Earthling leave home.

Earthlets wear special outfits to sleepovers called peejamas. They are called peejamas because sometimes Earthlets leak when they are asleep.

This is nobody's fault.
It can happen if the Earthlet is frightened . . .

. . . or in a strange bed . . .

. . . or worried about something.

Sometimes it happens for no reason known to man
or Martian.

When the Earthlet wakes up in a puddle, his face goes red. This is because he thinks he's the only one on the planet who wets the bed.

Wrong! His friends do it too! But they never tell because they think they're the only ones it happens to.

Parent Earthlings never shout if they find a bed puddle. This is because they leaked in their own beds a billion light years ago when they were young. Happily, Earthlets do not make puddles forever. When they are older, they stop leaking all by themselves.

Nowadays, Earthlets do not have to wake up in bed puddles. This is because Earthling Scientists have had the intelligence to invent pyjama pants.

Wise Earthlets wear these under their peejamas to prevent even the most mega-leaks.

Nobody knows they are wearing them, but now they can stay dry all night…

But they still can't stay QUIET!!!!

That is the end of today's lesson. Put your disguises on and get into the spaceship. We have been invited to a sleepover on Planet Earth. Please put on your pyjama pants before we land. The Earthlings are so funny, some of you are bound to wet yourselves.

Oops . . . I wish they made them in my size!

Important Messages for Earthling Parents

Bedwetting is a common childhood problem and affects nearly 10% of all 4-15 year olds at some stage. Remember, it is no one's fault - bedwetting is not caused by anything you or your child has done.

DryNites® has worked with children's authors, Jeanne Willis and Tony Ross to produce 'Dr Xargle's book of Earthlet Sleepovers'. This book is designed to help you discuss bedwetting with your child, and provide them with the support and encouragement they need.

Why is bedwetting happening?

There are a number of possible explanations for bedwetting including the birth of a younger sibling, starting a new school, being bullied, moving to a new house, a smaller than normal bladder or one that empties before it is full. However, it is important to remember that more often than not, there is no explanation - it just happens.

How can I help my child stay dry?

Most children do not need medication for bedwetting as it is a phase that they will grow out of. Until they do, there are a variety of ways in which you can help manage the situation including:

★ Encouraging your child to drink regularly throughout the day
★ Limiting the last drink to an hour before bedtime
★ Leaving the bathroom light on at night or putting a potty in their bedroom
★ Using DryNites® Pyjama Pants to ease the situation for both you and your child

Always remember to be optimistic and reassure your child that they are not alone. Your reassurance will help their confidence.

Sleepover Approved

DryNites® Pyjama Pants are absorbent pants that offer discreet night time protection so your child stays dry and comfortable throughout the night.

They are designed to be worn under nightwear and fit like real underwear so no one else needs to know they are there, giving your child the confidence and independence to combat any lack of control they may be feeling about bedwetting. The absorbent pad draws wetness away from the skin, whilst the moisture proof outer cover, leak guards and stretchable sides offer a comfortable snug fit. So not only will your child get a better night's rest, they will also feel confident in the morning.

DryNites® Pyjama Pants can be purchased from all major supermarkets and chemists.

They are available in 3 sizes for children aged:
★ 4-7 (medium/20-30kg),
★ 7-10 (large/30-40kg),
★ 10-15 (extra large/40-60kg).

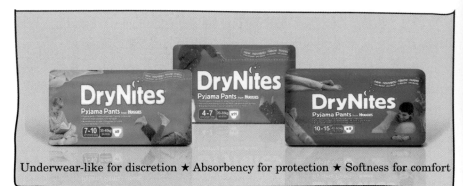

Underwear-like for discretion ★ Absorbency for protection ★ Softness for comfort

THE CUSTOMER: This coupon can be used in part payment for any pack of DryNites® Pyjama Pants. Only one coupon can be used for a single pack purchased. Do not embarrass your retailer by asking him to redeem it against another item, as he is not empowered to do so. Redemption value 0.01p.

THE RETAILER: Kimberly-Clark Ltd. will redeem this coupon at face value provided that it has ONLY been accepted in part payment for a pack of DryNites® Pyjama Pants. Coupons must be presented within three months of the stated valid until date. Kimberly-Clark Ltd. reserve the right to refuse payment against mis-redeemed coupons.
Coupon redemption to: NCH Dept 106, Corby, Northants NN17 1NN.

9 900519 851005

1000 9919099

® Registered Trademark of Kimberly-Clark Worldwide, Inc.

Further Help and Advice

For further advice on bedwetting,
please call the free phone bedwetting helpline.

0800 085 8189

DryNites® also provides help and information aimed specifically at children and parents on their website at

www.drynites.com

If you're still concerned, ask your Practice Nurse, GP or Health Visitor for advice.

® Registered Trademark of Kimberly-Clark Worldwide, Inc   © KCWW2004